C000042288

Disney's Tigger Annual

Editor: Lisa Carless   **Designer**: Tina Lamport

©Disney. Based on the Pooh stories by A.A. Milne. © The Pooh Properties Trust.
Published in Great Britain in 2000 by Egmont World Ltd., a division of Egmont Holdings Ltd,
Deanway Technology Centre,Wilmslow Road, Handforth, Cheshire SK9 3FB. Printed in Italy.
ISBN 0 7498 4870 7

£5.99
UK only

Hello, boys and girls!

Welcome to the Hundred Acre Wood - there's lots to do and see. You'll find lots of stories all about my friends and me! I hope you enjoy bouncing through this book!

We've hidden lots of objects in your annual. See how many you can find!

CONTENTS

The story of THE Tigger MOVIE

WALT DISNEY
PICTURES PRESENTS

1 It was a late autumn day and Tigger was happily bouncing through the Hundred Acre Wood. "How wonderful it is to be a Tigger," he said to himself, as he made his way to Pooh's house.

2 "Hiya, Buddy-boy! Wanna go bouncin'?" cried Tigger. "I would do, Tigger, but I'm in the middle of getting ready for winter," said Pooh Bear.

3 Tigger asked all his friends to come bouncing with him, but they were preparing for winter, too. So, Tigger went off on his own and bounced on a huge boulder which, in turn...

4 ...bounced right on to Eeyore's house and crushed it to pieces - just as he had finished putting on a new roof.

5

5 All the friends gathered to help lift the boulder. Rabbit made a contraption but Tigger came along, bounced on it and that broke, too! "No bouncing!" shouted Rabbit.

6 "I wish I had a family to bounce with," said Tigger to Owl, sadly. "You need to trace your family tree," said Owl.

7 Everyone started to feel for Tigger so they all decided to help look for his family. "You're rather stripey, but you don't look like a Tigger!" said Pooh to some bees in one of his favourite places - where his favourite food is!

8 Tigger then wrote a letter to his family but he didn't get a reply. To cheer Tigger up, Roo asked Owl to send a pretend reply.

9 Tigger was so very excited with his reply that he woke up all his friends to tell them! "They're all coming to visit - tomorrow!" he said. No one remembered Owl putting **that** part in the letter! "What are we going to do?" said Roo.

10 Tigger even started to build an extension to his house. Roo felt so guilty that he went to tell Tigger the truth about the letter, but he just didn't have the heart.

11 As Tigger prepared for a big family party, Roo and all of Tigger's friends agreed that they would have to pretend to be Tigger's family!

12 And that's what they did! They were soon having so much fun bouncing, that no one noticed a snow storm raging outside. Then, all of a sudden, Roo gave a huge bounce and his mask came off!

13 "None of you are my family!" said Tigger, heartbroken. "Well, I know they're out there somewhere - I'm going to find them." With that, Tigger went out into the cold night. "Come back!" cried Roo.

14 His friends organised a search party to find Tigger. But the storm was getting worse! "Tigger!" they all cried.

15 Eventually, they found Tigger. "We're really your family and we all love you," said Pooh.

16 Tigger was so pleased to see all his friends. "You guys **are** my family!" he said, with a big smile.

Autumn leaves

Count how many of each kind of leaf is blowing around in the big picture of Tigger and write your answers in the empty box beside each small picture.

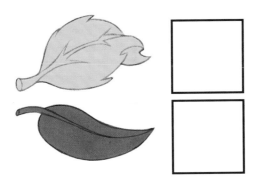

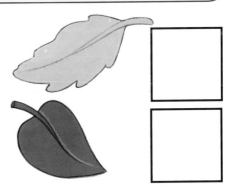

Long lost family!

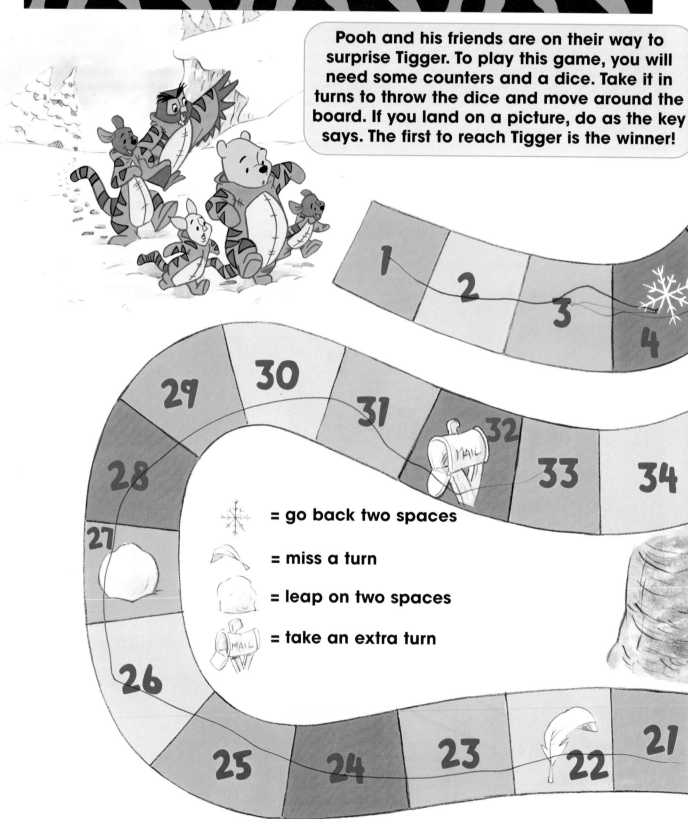

Pooh and his friends are on their way to surprise Tigger. To play this game, you will need some counters and a dice. Take it in turns to throw the dice and move around the board. If you land on a picture, do as the key says. The first to reach Tigger is the winner!

= go back two spaces

= miss a turn

= leap on two spaces

= take an extra turn

Tigger's surprise!

Tigger's here to show you how to make a super puzzle. You will need some card, paste, a small coffee-jar lid, two silver balls (used for cake decoration), round-ended scissors, a pencil and some cling-film.

1. Paste this page on to a piece of card and carefully cut out the Tigger picture.

2. Using the point of a pencil, make two holes where Tigger's eyes should be.

3. Paste the card inside the coffee-jar lid and let it dry. Then, put the two silver balls inside.

4. Cover with cling-film, taping it firmly at the back of the lid. Now, see if you can shake the silver balls on to Tigger's eyes.

The mystery box

1 Tigger saw Rabbit walking along, carrying some parcels and a very special-looking box. "What's in that box?" he asked. "It's a secret," Rabbit told him.

2 Now Tigger was even more curious. "I'll follow Rabbit and when he opens the box I can see what's inside."

3 But Rabbit was carrying so many parcels, he didn't notice when the special one fell off the pile. He just kept walking. "Goody! Now I can open it," said Tigger, running over to the box.

4 But just as he was about to pick up the box, it moved away. "Hey," gasped Tigger. He tried to pick it up again but it moved away again.

5 Every time Tigger went to pick up the box, it moved away. So he bounced a big bounce and grabbed it. "I've got it!" he shouted. "I've got it!"

6 Then Tigger noticed a piece of string tied to the box. "What's this?" he wondered, pulling it. Rabbit came flying out of the bushes, holding the other end of the string!

7 "Rabbit!" gasped Tigger as Rabbit fell on top of him. "So that's why the parcel kept moving! You were pulling it!"

8 "Well, I've got the box now, so I'm going to open it!" said Tigger. He pulled off the paper. "Don't open that!" shouted Rabbit, in a fluster.

9 "Ouch!" yelled Tigger as a trick boxing glove sprang out and hit him on the chin. "Ha, ha!" laughed Rabbit. "Tricked you again, Tigger! I'm a much better joker than you!" Poor old Tigger!

Piglet's colouring

Colour this picture with your crayons. Look at the little picture to see what colours to use.

● Can you see what is in the mystery box?

16

● Who can you see in the picture?

What colour is the boxing glove?

How many trick boxing gloves can you see?

How many jigsaw pieces are there?

Can you count the stones?

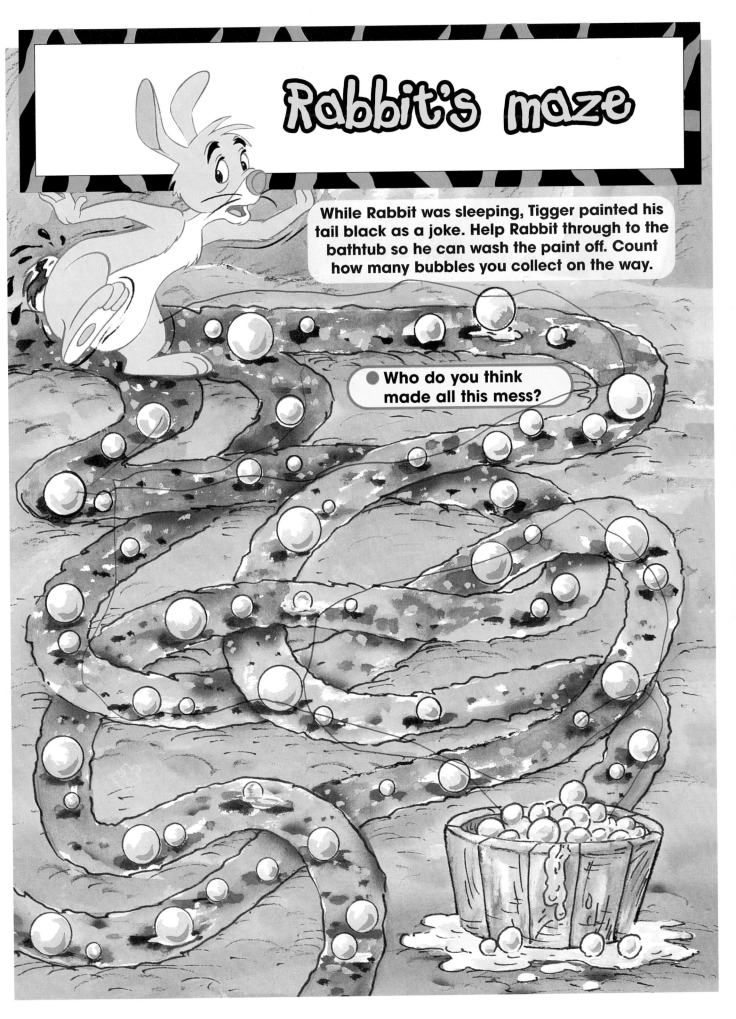

Rabbit's maze

While Rabbit was sleeping, Tigger painted his tail black as a joke. Help Rabbit through to the bathtub so he can wash the paint off. Count how many bubbles you collect on the way.

Who do you think made all this mess?

The scarf fuddle

1 Eeyore had caught a cold. His throat was so sore he could hardly speak. "I wish I had a scarf," he croaked to Tigger.

2 "Leave it to me," said Tigger bouncing off. Eeyore was peased. "How kind," he thought, "Tigger's gone to fetch a scarf to keep my neck warm."

3 But Tigger returned wearing a funny hat and carrying some balloons and streamers! "Surprise!" he said. Eeyore was very confused.

4 Piglet and Pooh were watching and laughed. But Eeyore didn't think it was funny. "What are you doing?" he croaked. "You wanted to laugh," replied Tigger.

5 "I said scarf not laugh!" croaked Eeyore. "Oh, sorry!" said Tigger. "I think Christopher Robin's got one," said Pooh.

6 So Piglet, Pooh and Tigger went to see Christopher Robin. "I wonder why Eeyore wants a giraffe," said Piglet. "Perhaps he wants to play with it to cheer himself up," said Pooh.

7 Christopher Robin lent them his toy giraffe and they hurried back to Eeyore with it. "We've got you one!" shouted Tigger. Eeyore groaned when he saw the toy giraffe.

8 "I said scarf, not giraffe!" He whispered. "Oh, I see! I have one at home, but I'll need some help carrying it," said Pooh.

9 Pooh, Piglet and Tigger hurried to Pooh's house. But instead of fetching a scarf, they started to fill up Pooh's bath!

22

10 Tigger, Piglet and Pooh carried the bath back to Eeyore. "Here you are," said Pooh. "A nice, warm bath!" "With oodles of bubbles in it," added Tigger.

11 Eeyore couldn't believe it! "Oh, no!" he croaked, shaking his head, miserably. Kanga and Roo were passing and heard him. "Goodness, your throat sounds sore," said Kanga.

12 "Here, wrap this warm scarf around your neck," she said, giving her scarf to Eeyore. "That'll make you feel better." "Thank you," he smiled, happily. "That's just what I need!"

Drawing with Piglet

Oh, dear, Piglet is in a muddle - he's forgotten what he's drawn!
Can you colour in the dotted shape to see what the picture is?

Tigger's surprise!

Here's Tigger to show you how to make a super fuddles and muddles jigsaw. All you need is a picture from an old comic or magazine, a pen, some paste and some round-ended scissors. You will need to ask a grown-up to help.

1 First, paste the picture on to some card, and draw on some wavy lines to divide it into jigsaw shapes.

2 Then, with your scissors, carefully cut along all the wavy lines.

3 Now, muddle and fuddle up the pieces and try to put the jigsaw all back together again!

Fuddles and muddles rhyme

When Eeyore caught a cold,

We could barely hear him speak.

He tried and tried and tried,

But his voice was much too meek.

● Why are Pooh
and Tigger
carrying a bath?

Can you find these things in the picture?
Put a tick in the box when you have
found each one.

26

● How many balloons can you see?

His friends all brought him things,

And they tried to make him laugh.

Then Eeyore gently croaked,

"I just need a nice, warm scarf!"

● What colour is the giraffe?

● What's the matter with Eeyore?

Another muddle

"Are you sitting comfortably, Pooh?" asked Christopher Robin.
"Then I'll tell you a story…"

Eeyore looked so poorly that Kanga took him home with her, to look after him. She gave him a warm drink and a spoonful of her special honey throat medicine then tucked him up in Roo's bed. "Now you stay here until you're better," she said. "Roo can sleep in my room." "Thank you," croaked Eeyore. He snuggled down in bed and closed his eyes and was soon sound asleep.
Early the next morning, Tigger came bouncing by. "Hey, Roo," he cried, knocking on Roo's window. "Do you want to play ball?" But, of course, Roo wasn't in his room, Eeyore was. Eeyore heard Tigger shout and mumbled back, sleepily. Tigger thought the mumble was Roo agreeing to play. "Meet you at the big oak tree then!" he said and bounced off. Tigger waited for a long time at the big oak tree for Roo. But Roo never came. "Maybe he's ill," thought Tigger. "Poor, Roo! I'll have to tell everyone so we can all make him a get-well card."

"Thanks for thinking of me," he croaked. "I'm feeling better already."

"What a muddle!" smiled Pooh. "Did Eeyore get better soon?" "Oh, yes, another dose of Kanga's medicine and his throat was much better," said Christopher Robin. "All those muddles have made my brain fuddled," yawned Pooh. "I think I'll have a nap now. Goodnight, Christopher Robin." "Goodnight, dear Pooh. Sweet dreams."

So Tigger told his friends about Roo being ill and they all made him a get-well card. Then, Tigger and the others went to take the cards to Roo. They were all very surprised when Tigger knocked on the door and Roo answered it. "I thought you were ill!" said Tigger.
"I'm not! Eeyore is," said Roo. "He's in my bed."
They all decided to give the get-well cards to Eeyore instead. He was really pleased.

29

Buzzing busy bees

Try to put these pictures in the right
order to tell the story of what happened when Pooh,
Piglet and Eeyore went in search of Tigger's family.

30

Rabbit's maze

Rabbit has lost his spade. With your finger, trace which path he should take to find it. Count how many carrots and cabbages you collect on the way. How many carrots are there all together?

Tigger's favourite friends

Trace along the tangled paths to see who found Tigger sitting on a branch of a tree.

Answer: Kanga found Tigger up the tree.

Looking for thistles

1 Eeyore needed cheering up. "I think I'll have a tasty snack of **thistles**," he said. But when he went to his thistle patch he found that all the thistles had gone.

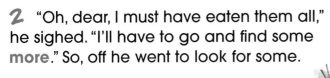

2 "Oh, dear, I must have eaten them all," he sighed. "I'll have to go and find some **more**." So, off he went to look for some.

3 Eeyore was looking behind a log for thistles when Tigger bounced along. "Oops, **sorry**!" he said as he landed on Eeyore. "I just didn't see you there!"

4 "Hello Tigger," sighed Eeyore, picking himself back up. "What are you doing?" asked Tigger. "Looking for some thistles for my **lunch**," Eeyore told him.

5 "Leave it to me," said Tigger. "I'll soon find some." He bounced around, looking for thistles. "**There**!" he shouted, pushing past Eeyore and knocking him over.

6 But they weren't thistles, after all. "Never mind, **keep looking**, we'll find some soon," said Tigger. "I think I'll look by myself," groaned Eeyore. "It's safer!"

7 "Maybe I should have something else for lunch," said Eeyore, as Tigger bounced into him again. "I'll bet there are some thistles over **here**," shouted Tigger.

8 Tigger ran over to some bushes. But he didn't see that there was a basket lying in front of them and he tripped over it. "**Ouch**!" he cried as he fell right over the basket and...

9 ...landed in a pile of thistles! "Oh, **good**!" smiled Eeyore. "You've found some thistles and a basket to carry them in. Well done, Tigger!"

Piglet's colouring

Colour this picture with your crayons. Look at the little picture to see what colours to use.

How many clouds can you see?

What is Eeyore holding?

● What would make you say, *Ouch?*

● What has Tigger landed on?

Hello, everyone, I'm going to tell you all about hedgehogs. Hedgehogs have whiskers and a pointed nose. Their bodies are covered in spines and as soon as they sense danger, they roll up into a prickly ball.

Watch out! I'm prickly!

An adult hedgehog has more than 5,000 needle-sharp spines. The spines are just stiff, hollow hairs.

● Have you ever seen a hedgehog?

● How many hedgehogs can you count on this page?

Budge up!

Baby **hedgehogs** have soft whitish spines. Before they're born, the spines are folded flat under their skin. They pop up and stick out a few hours after birth.

● Can you think of another animal you might find in your garden?

When the weather starts to get cold, **hedgehogs** build a nest in the bottom of a hedge or in a pile of dried leaves and hibernate for the winter.

● Does this hedgehog look asleep or awake?

Is it summer yet?

What's changed?

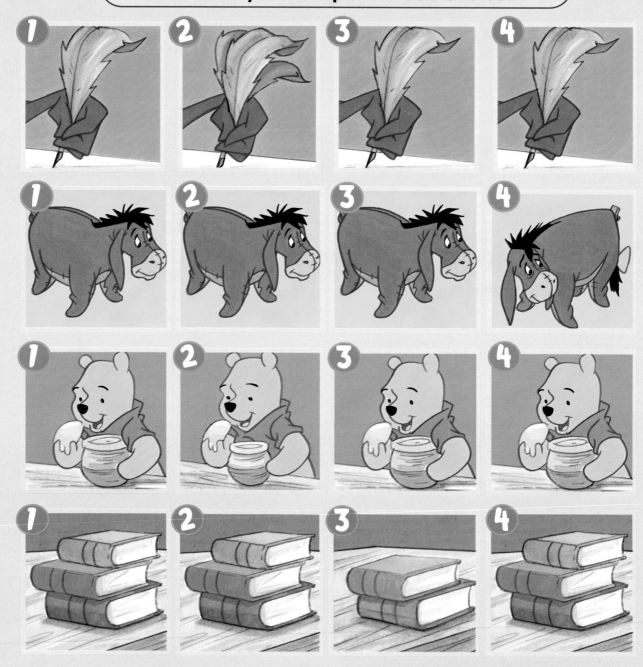

Answers: Row 1, picture 2; row 2, picture 4; row 3, picture 2; row 4, picture 3.

Family figures

Can you help Tigger and Roo to find five of Owl's family pictures hidden in the picture?

Drawing with Piglet

Piglet wants to draw a picture to give to Pooh. Can you think of Pooh's favourite thing and draw a picture of it?

Muddy feet

1 Rabbit was busy digging his carrot patch when Tigger came by. "**Hello, Rabbit**," Tigger cried, bouncing into the garden.

2 But Tigger splashed in the mud and made muddy footprints all between the carrots! Rabbit was cross! "Look at all this mud!" he cried.

3 "Sorry! I'll clean it up!" said Tigger, bouncing off to Rabbit's kitchen to fetch a mop. "**Stop!**" shouted Rabbit. You'll make my kitchen muddy!"

4 But it was too late! Tigger spilled water all over the floor and Rabbit slipped on it! "**Aargh!**" he yelled.

5 "Now you've made a mess in the kitchen, too!" Rabbit cried. "**Out!** I'll have to mop the floor!" "Okay, I'm going," said Tigger.

6 "I'll **clean up** the garden as a surprise for Rabbit," thought Tigger. Can you see what he's doing? Do you think Rabbit will be pleased?

7 Rabbit wasn't pleased. In fact, he was so angry he stamped his feet and jumped up and down! "Look at this mess, **Tigger**!" he yelled.

8 Rabbit was just about to clean the path himself when it started to rain. "Oh, no, **rain**!" he groaned. He and Tigger ran for shelter.

9 "Well, at least the rain has cleaned my path," smiled Rabbit. "And my **feet**!" laughed Tigger. "Now everything's clean again!"

45

Rabbit's maze

Help Rabbit through the maze to reach his mop so he can clean up. Count how many muddy footprints you pass on the way.

Tigger's surprise!

Tigger and Piglet are playing the 'Raindrop Race'. Would you like to play it, too? You can play it on your own or with a friend.

Next time it rains, go over to the window and choose two raindrops running down the glass. Decide which one you think will get to the bottom of the window first and watch them race down the window. Will your raindrop win? If it does, the rain is supposed to stop and the sun come out!

Race to the gate

Can you work out who reaches the gate in the fastest time? Trace along the lines, adding the seconds according to the key below.

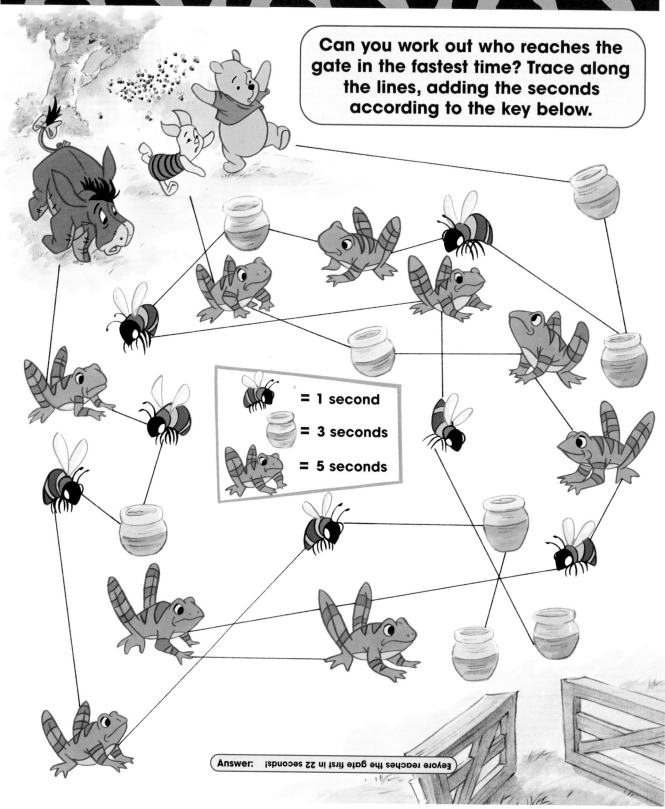

= 1 second

= 3 seconds

= 5 seconds

Answer: Eeyore reaches the gate first in 22 seconds!

Match the shadows

As a terrible blizzard raged, Tigger searched for his family tree. Can you make three pairs, by pairing up the tree shadows that are the same?

1

2

3

4

5

6

Answers: Trees 1 and 4 match, trees 2 and 6 match and trees 3 and 5 match.

It's party time!

Look carefully at Tigger's party scene and then see if you can answer the questions below.

How many 🧁 can you count?

How many ● can you count?

How many 🎉 can you count?

How many 🥤 can you count?

How many 🎂 can you count?

How many 🕯 can you count?

Counting with Owl

Count the objects and circle the correct number at the bottom of the page.

Count the frames with pictures in them.

How many frames without a picture can you count?

Are there three or four cards?

TO MY FRIEND

1 2 3 4 5 6